Wonderfully Made

enjoying life *with* God's special gift

Made

thegoodbook
COMPANY

Wonderfully Made Handbook
© The Good Book Company, 2015.

Also available: Wonderfully Made DVD

Published by
The Good Book Company Ltd.
Tel (UK): 0333 123 0880
Tel (US): 866 244 2165
International: +44 (0) 208 942 0880
Email (UK): info@thegoodbook.co.uk
Email (US): info@thegoodbook.com

Websites:
UK: www.thegoodbook.co.uk
North America: www.thegoodbook.com
Australia: www.thegoodbook.com.au
New Zealand: www.thegoodbook.co.nz

ISBN: 9781910307175

Design by André Parker / ninefootone creative

Printed in the Czech Republic

Wonderfully Made

enjoying life with God's special gift

Mary Winter
and Rachel Jones

thegoodbook
COMPANY

Contents

Welcome to Wonderfully Made!

The Bible says that our children are wonderfully made—and holding your newborn baby, it's not hard to see why. But what comes next is an emotional rollercoaster of highs and lows: side-splitting silliness and sleepless nights; heart-swelling pride and mind-numbing boredom. No wonder so many of us feel daunted and unprepared!

For lots of mums, toddler group has always been a great place to get together and chat about the concerns we face every day, and share ideas and tips we've found useful. There'll certainly be lots of space for that in this course! But we hope that *Wonderfully Made* is also a springboard to get you discussing some of the bigger questions you might have about the task of raising little humans, and get you thinking about who we are and why we're here. That's why we'll consider one of the foundational teachings of the Bible: that our children have been made "in God's image" by a Creator who loves them.

Whatever you believe, this course isn't about trying to give you all the answers, or making you feel inadequate. It's about supporting each other as we figure out how to survive as parents of young children.

How to use this handbook

 ## Watch

Each session we hear from a mum about her parenting experience, before watching a short talk from Mary Winter. You can scribble down notes or questions in the space provided, or just sit back and watch.

 ## Discuss

A chance to share your thoughts and ideas on the week's topic. Everyone will come to this course with their own unique set of experiences; so be honest and get stuck in!

 ## Try this at home

Ideas to help you put into practice what you've learned—from parenting tips to fun activities to try with your toddler. Not everything will be suitable for your little one, so don't beat yourself up about what you are or aren't doing. Some of the best suggestions will come from the other parents sitting next to you!

 ## Going further

If you'd like to think a little further about the "big questions" raised in each session, there's a passage from the Bible to read and a couple of questions to help you mull it over. If you've never read the Bible before, don't worry—it's not about knowing all the right answers!

Discussion 1

Introduction:
So many questions

 ## *Watch*

- The hardest thing about being a parent is…

- So many questions!

- Our children are wonderfully made.

Discuss

What do you think is the hardest thing about being a new parent?

....

....

....

What were some of the practical questions you had when you were dealing with a new baby? What about now?

....

....

....

Where did you look for answers to those questions?

....

....

Do you have any "bigger" life questions that you would like to talk over in the following weeks?

....

....

....

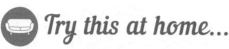

Try this at home...

- **Ask your parents or grandparents about their experience of raising you!** What did they most enjoy about being a parent? What might they do differently if they had another chance? What do they wish they'd known before they became a parent?

- **Make a family photo tree.** Include all those people who are important in your child's life, not just immediate family—friends, godparents, and those who love and support your family.

- **Keep a journal** (or maybe even write a blog!). This doesn't have to be an everyday burden, but it can help to lend perspective on the daily struggles. Force yourself to be positive, as well as honest about the negatives. Reading back and seeing how your child (and you) have changed and grown will be a real joy—and can help you to remember that each stage will eventually end!

 # Going further

This is a passage from the Bible; it's a song from the book of Psalms, a collection of songs written to and about God. The writer is talking to God.

> *¹³ For you created my inmost being;*
>> *you knit me together in my mother's womb.*
> *¹⁴ I praise you because I am fearfully and wonderfully made;*
>> *your works are wonderful,*
>> *I know that full well.*
> *¹⁵ My frame was not hidden from you*
>> *when I was made in the secret place,*
>> *when I was woven together in the depths of the earth.*
> *¹⁶ Your eyes saw my unformed body;*
>> *all the days ordained for me were written in your book*
>> *before one of them came to be.*

Psalm 139 v 13-16

Think about it:

What does this Bible passage have to say about how our children were made?

....

....

....

When the writer thinks about that, what does it make him do?
(Look at the start of verse 14.)

....

....

We don't really know what will happen to our children tomorrow, let alone
in 20 or 30 years' time! But look at verse 16. How does that make you feel?

....

....

Suppose God does know your child as well as this psalm says he does. What
would you say to him?

....

....

....

Wonderfully made... in God's image

 Watch

～ Our children bear our image.

～ "God created mankind in his own image."

～ Valued and loved by God?

Discuss

How are you like your own parents?

....

....

In what ways are your children like you?

....

....

....

In what ways would you like your children to take after you? What aspects of your character do you *not* want them to inherit?

....

....

What do you think of the idea that God made each one of us?

....

....

Try this at home...

- **Make photo memories.** Some parents make a point of taking a similar photo of each of their children doing the same thing at the same age (eg: their last night sleeping in their Moses basket, or in a swing at 12 months old). It's nice to look through them and see the similarities— and differences—between each of your children. Or maybe there's an embarrassing baby photo of yours that you could recreate with your little one!

- **Copy-cat.** Children love copying what mum and dad are doing. Why not encourage them to "help" you with household chores? Sweeping up, hanging up washing, wiping the table, DIY…

- **What will they become?** Make some predictions about what you think your child will be like when they grow up. What job will they do? Where will they live? What will they enjoy doing? And what will the world be like? Get other relatives to join in too. Put the predictions in an envelope in a safe place—they might make interesting (and surprising!) reading on your child's 21st birthday.

Going further

All the bits of the Bible used in the main talks of this course are taken from its very first two chapters. This part of the book of Genesis was deliberately written to be beautifully poetic. You might have your doubts about how much of it could have literally happened; but Christians believe that Genesis can still teach us truths about God, ourselves and why the world is the way it is.

Genesis begins with God creating the world. We pick up the story after God has made the earth, plants and animals…

> 26 Then God said, "Let us make mankind in our image, in our likeness, so that they may rule over the fish in the sea and the birds in the sky, over the livestock and all the wild animals, and over all the creatures that move along the ground."
> 27 So God created mankind in his own image,
>   in the image of God he created them;
>   male and female he created them.
> 28 God blessed them and said to them, "Be fruitful and increase in number; fill the earth and subdue it. Rule over the fish in the sea and the birds in the sky and over every living creature that moves on the ground."
> 29 Then God said, "I give you every seed-bearing plant on the face of the whole earth and every tree that has fruit with seed in it. They will be yours for food. 30 And to all the beasts of the earth and all the birds in the sky and all the creatures that move along the ground—everything that has the breath of life in it—I give

every green plant for food." And it was so.
31 God saw all that he had made, and it was very good.

Genesis 1 v 26-31

Think about it:

How many times does it say God made mankind in his image?

....

....

What does God tell the people to do?

....

....

Look at everything God gives the people (v 28-30). How does that sound to you? Looking at these verses, how would you describe God's character?

....

....

....

What did God think of the creation—and the people—he had made (v 31)?

....

....

Wonderfully made...
to be creative

 ## Watch

- Kids love making things!

- "God created the heavens and the earth."

- The world around us tells us something about God.

- Expressions of the image of God within us.

- How does this help us?
    1) Encourage our children to explore.

    2) We're creative too!

Discuss

How does your child most enjoy using their imagination and sense of creativity? What do they like doing?

....

....

Suppose that God did create the natural world. What beautiful, amazing or just plain weird part of creation would you congratulate him on?

....

....

What do you make of the explanation that humans are creative because we're made in God's image? Do you agree?

....

....

When do you find yourself getting bored? When you feel like that, what do you do?

....

....

Try this at home...

- **Make edible finger paint.** This craft is perfect for encouraging your child to explore with all of their senses. Mix 2 cups of corn flour with 1 cup of cold water. Pour in 4.5 cups of boiling water—add it a cup at a time and keep stirring! It should come to a consistency like custard. Separate into different pots and add food colouring. Then let your child get creative with it!

- **Make a masking-tape racetrack.** Bored of pushing your toddler's cars round the same toy garage? Set them free by marking out a racetrack around the room using masking tape. Then zoom those cars across the carpet, over the sofa, under the table…

- **Choose a project for you!** What would you like to do? It doesn't have to be an amazing creation—maybe just getting to the end of that trashy novel you started months ago, or watching a film the whole way through. Some people find setting a target helps them get going. Tell each other your creative goals and ask next week if you've managed to get round to it yet!

- **Make a weekly schedule.** Some mums find a weekly schedule can be helpful in breaking up the week and keeping every day a little bit different. It's important to schedule in some time for yourself, as well as for all the jobs which inevitably need doing! A schedule can help you think about having a balanced week, which will benefit you and your children.

 *Going further*

This passage is taken from the book of Psalms, a collection of songs written to and about God.

> ¹ LORD, our Lord, how majestic is your name in all the earth!
>   You have set your glory
>   in the heavens.
> ² Through the praise of children and infants
>   you have established a stronghold against your enemies,
>   to silence the foe and the avenger.
> ³ When I consider your heavens,
>   the work of your fingers,
>   the moon and the stars,
>   which you have set in place,
> ⁴ what is mankind that you are mindful of them,
>   human beings that you care for them?
> ⁵ You have made them a little lower than the angels
>   and crowned them with glory and honour.
> ⁶ You made them rulers over the works of your hands;

you put everything under their feet:
  ⁷ all flocks and herds,
      and the animals of the wild,
  ⁸ the birds in the sky,
      and the fish in the sea,
      all that swim the paths of the seas.
  ⁹ LORD, our Lord,
      how majestic is your name in all the earth!

Psalm 8

Think about it:

What are some of the things this psalm says God has created? (Look at verses 3, 7 and 8.)

....

....

....

How has God shown how glorious he is (v 1)?

....

....

Look at verses 4-6. Do we matter to God? Why do you think that is?

....

....

How does thinking about this make the writer feel (v 3-4)?

....

....

Wonderfully made...
to rest

Watch

— Tiredness is a real issue.

— When God finished creating, he rested!

— "By the seventh day God had finished the work he had been doing; so on the seventh day he rested from all his work" (Genesis 2 v 2).

— Finding joy in routines of daily life.

— Tips for coping with sleepless nights:
- Remember sleepless nights won't last for ever
- Rest when you can
- Try to eat well and take a little exercise
- Cut yourself some slack!

— Finding ways to refresh, relax and laugh!

 *Discuss*

Does your child sleep well? What have you found helps?

....

....

In what ways does tiredness affect you?

....

....

"When we read that God rested, it means that he took the time to enjoy what he had made." How could you get in the habit of taking time out of the business of day-to-day life to really enjoy it?

....

....

....

What do you like doing to relax and refresh?

....

....

 Try this at home...

- **Bed-time routines**. Most parents know that these are a good idea, but it's another thing to implement one consistently. Don't worry about what's not worked before; just make a fresh start—bath-time, story-time, bedtime. Maybe you could do with a bedtime routine too! It's easy to think: "I'll just check my emails..." and before you know it, two hours have slipped by! Set a time when the screens go off and you call it a night.

- **Count your blessings!** Getting into the habit of being grateful for the little things helps us to stay positive, even when it's been "one of those days". Give it a go this week—each day, take two minutes out to write down something good, fortunate or funny that happened to you (my bus arrived just as I got to the bus stop; my son remembered to say thank you…).

Sunday

....

....

Monday

....

....

Tuesday

....

....

Wednesday

....

....

Thursday

....

....

Friday

....

....

Saturday

....

....

- **Take a bath.** Enjoying a nice, relaxing bath can be a great way to unwind. Why not try a weird and wonderful homemade bath recipe? Try adding 1 or 2 cups of milk and half a cup of honey for an ancient-Egyptian-themed soak; or chuck in 4-6 teabags and let your skin benefit from all those antioxidants... Alternatively, you might want to stick with the Radox.

- **"Alone time".** Don't be afraid build some playing-alone time into your toddler's routine—maybe in a playpen or port-a-cot with some toys or books. Learning to occupy themselves is a really valuable skill and will give you some much needed moments to yourself.

 # Going further

This passage is from Mark, which is an account of Jesus' life. Jesus' friends ("the apostles") have just come back from a busy trip.

> ³⁰ *The apostles gathered around Jesus and reported to him all they had done and taught.* ³¹ *Then, because so many people were coming and going that they did not even have a chance to eat, he said to them, "Come with me by yourselves to a quiet place and get some rest."*
>
> ³² *So they went away by themselves in a boat to a solitary place.* ³³ *But many who saw them leaving recognised them and ran on foot from all the towns and got there ahead of them.* ³⁴ *When Jesus landed and saw a large crowd, he had compassion on them, because they were like sheep without a shepherd. So he began teaching them many things.*
>
> Mark 6 v 30-34

Think about it:

Things are pretty hectic for Jesus and his friends! What does Jesus encourage them to do (v 31)?

....

....

Something gets in the way of Jesus' R&R. Does he seem annoyed? Is that how you react when your plans for time out get interrupted?

....

....

What might it mean that the people were "like sheep without a shepherd" (v 34)?

....

....

Jesus knows what his friends need (a good rest!)—so he takes them to a solitary place. And he knows what the crowd needs (a shepherd to guide them)—so he starts teaching them. What words would you use to describe Jesus, based on this story?

....

....

Discussion 5

Wonderfully made... for relationships

 ## Watch

– Parenthood can be lonely.

– "It is not good for the man to be alone" (Genesis 2 v 18).

– We're created for relationships.

– How does this help us?
  • We're designed for a relationship with God. It's possible to have a friendship with God.

  • We're designed for relationships with each other. We want to teach our children to value friendship.

Discuss

At what times do you feel lonely? What helps you deal with that? Who do you have to support you?

....

....

What are some of the ways in which you motivate yourself to get out and about and relating to others?

....

....

Have you ever thought of God as wanting a relationship with you before? Do you think it matters?

....

....

....

How can we, as a group, better help parents who feel isolated?

....

....

Try this at home...

- **Talking targets.** Each time you come to toddler group, challenge yourself to have at least one conversation with another adult that's not about your children.

- **Get social.** Invite other parents and their children round to your home for coffee. There are probably lots of people here who it would be good to get to know better. Inviting them into your home is a great way to do that. Go on—invite them now!

- **Talk about TV.** As you read books and watch TV with your toddler, make a point of chatting about what you see happening. Ask questions like: "Are the characters being good friends to each other?"; "Was that a kind thing to do?"; "How would you feel if that happened to you?"

- **Research some of the activities that are going on in your local area.** The library, the leisure centre, the park, churches and the cinema are all likely to have special activities for parents and pre-schoolers.

- **Check out an evening class.** If you've got childcare available, it can be great to get out and about without your little one, too. Evening classes are great for stretching your mind (or your body).

 *Going further*

This week, let's take another closer look at Genesis.

> ¹⁸ The LORD God said, "It is not good for the man to be alone. I will make a helper suitable for him."
>
> ¹⁹ Now the LORD God had formed out of the ground all the wild animals and all the birds in the sky. He brought them to the man to see what he would name them; and whatever the man called each living creature, that was its name. ²⁰ So the man gave names to all the livestock, the birds in the sky and all the wild animals.
>
> But for Adam no suitable helper was found. ²¹ So the LORD God caused the man to fall into a deep sleep; and while he was sleeping, he took one of the man's ribs and then closed up the place with flesh. ²² Then the LORD God made a woman from the rib he had taken out of the man, and he brought her to the man.
>
> ²³ The man said,
>
> "This is now bone of my bones
>   and flesh of my flesh;

she shall be called 'woman',
for she was taken out of man."

Genesis 2 v 18-23

Think about it:

We've already seen that God described his creation as "good". But what's "not good" here?

....

During this course, we've thought about how humans are different to anything else in creation, because we're made in God's image. How do we see that to be true in these verses? (Look at verse 20.)

....

....

How does the man react when he sees the woman?

....

....

....

God sees that the man needs a companion, and then custom-makes one for him! How would you describe God's character, based on these verses?

....

....

....

Discussion 6

Wonderfully made...
to communicate

Watch

➤ It's frustrating when we can't communicate.

➤ God speaks:
- *I have given you every tree in this wonderful garden to eat from...*
- *... but you must not eat from this one tree...*
- *... if you eat from it you will certainly die.*

➤ Jesus is God showing himself to us.

➤ God wants a two-way relationship with us.

 # Discuss

What was your child's first word? (Or what do you expect it will be?)

....

Have you ever tried communicating with God? How? What happened?

....

....

....

When talking with your child, do you ever struggle to get the balance right between speaking to them and listening to them? Which way do you tend to err?

....

....

....

 # Try this at home...

- **Keep a little notebook of funny things people in your family say.** Toddlers often come out with hilarious things, but mummy and daddy sometimes mix up their words too! This little book will be great fun to read back over as a family in years to come.

- **Older children will enjoy listening games.** Try picking a "word for the day"; it could be a colour or number. Your child gets a sticker for every time they hear it used.

- **Communicate clearly.** Often trying to get our child to do something is like speaking to a brick wall! But keeping a few things in mind can help: Make sure you have their attention before giving them the instruction. Make instructions simple and clear—don't overwhelm your toddler with a barrage of words. When they're old enough, get your child to repeat what you've said back to you, to show that they've understood.

- **Listen.** Even when your child has very few words, you can model what it means to be a good listener. When possible, stop what you're doing and give them your full attention when they are communicating with you. That way, you can expect them to do the same when you are speaking to them.

- **They need to be part of your world.** It's good for your little one to be exposed to adult conversation; eating together round the dinner table with friends and family is a great way of doing this, even if you're only able to do it occasionally!

 *Going further*

The book of John is a part of the Bible which tells the story of Jesus' life. In this section, Jesus is talking with some of his friends (or disciples).

> [6] *Jesus answered, "I am the way and the truth and the life. No one comes to the Father except through me.* [7] *If you really know me, you will know my Father as well. From now on, you do know him and have seen him."*
>
> [8] *Philip said, "Lord, show us the Father and that will be enough for us."*
>
> [9] *Jesus answered: "Don't you know me, Philip, even after I have been among you such a long time? Anyone who has seen me has seen the Father. How can you say, 'Show us the Father'?* [10] *Don't you believe that I am in the Father, and that the Father is in me? The words I say to you I do not speak on my own authority. Rather, it is the Father, living in me, who is doing his work."*

John 14 v 6-10

Think about it:

According to Jesus, how can people know God (the Father)?

....

....

Jesus' friend Philip doesn't seem to get it though!

What three things does Jesus claim to be in verse 6?

....

....

....

What might Jesus be talking about when he says that he is "the life"?

....

....

....

What, or who, do you think Jesus is "the way" to?

....

....

....

Wonderfully made... but spoiled

Watch

- Why is it so hard to get our children to do as they've been asked?!

- Why are our relationships so hard to get right?

- The first people chose to ignore God's warning.

- God's image in us is spoiled.

- If we want to know more about God, we need to look at Jesus.

Discuss

How do you deal with your child's misbehaviour? What have you found that works? What doesn't?

....

....

....

Do you agree that God's image in humans has been spoiled? Or do you think we are mostly good?

....

....

....

....

Why do you think God would want to fix his relationship with humans, when we're the ones who messed things up?

....

....

....

Looking back over this course, has there been anything that's surprised you? Has it made you change your mind about anything?

....

....

....

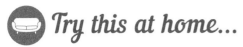

Try this at home...

- **Discover new methods.** Sticker charts, time outs, naughty steps: different parents have lots of different methods of rewarding good behaviour and disciplining bad behaviour. Ask around and swap ideas.

- **Saying sorry.** Don't be afraid to say sorry to your child when you get things wrong—and let them see you apologising to other adults, too. Show them what forgiveness looks like and model restored relationships—this will help them grow into adults who can move past the inevitable hurts and mistakes that will come their way.

- **Cooking challenge.** Here's a fun cooking challenge for older children: Find the most deformed fruit or vegetable you can at the shop and make something delicious out of it together when you get home.

Going further

This part of the Bible is taken from a letter sent to Christians in Rome, written about 20 years after Jesus lived on earth.

> *23 All have sinned and fall short of the glory of God, 24 and all are justified freely by his grace through the redemption that came by Christ Jesus.*
>
> **Romans 3 v 23-24**

Over this course, we've thought about how we were designed to reflect God's glory. But what's the problem, according to verse 23?

....

....

Are there any exceptions to this? Does this include your child? Does this include you?

....

....

Can you think of a way in which you've fallen short of God's perfect standards recently?

....

....

....

"Justified ... grace ... redemption". These are all huge concepts! But what it's saying is that God has provided a solution to mend our spoiled relationship with him. Who does that solution come by?

....

What next?

I hope you've enjoyed taking part in *Wonderfully Made* as you've shared some of the joys and frustrations of parenthood together. Perhaps it's also got you thinking about God and how he is already a part of your family life. If you want to find out more about what a healthy relationship with God looks like, or you want to help your child get to know the God who made them, here are some suggestions for what to do next...

Invest in a children's Bible

One way that you can start teaching your child about our loving God is by reading to them from a children's Bible. There are lots of children's Bibles which re-tell Bible stories in a simple way that children can understand, with wonderful illustrations. The person running your group will be able to suggest a good children's Bible and where to get it. You might like to consider *The Beginner's Bible*, *The Jesus Storybook Bible* or *The Big Picture Story Bible*, all of which are available from www.thegoodbook.co.uk.

Start to go regularly to a local church

Another great way of introducing your child to God is by bringing them with you to church. Lots of churches run a Sunday School, children's groups and crèches for young children. There will also be a part of the service where the Bible is explained for adults, too. This is about much more than just learning things; church is supposed to be like a big, extended family. You should find a warm welcome for you and your child, and lots of people who want to get to know you and support you—especially if you're feeling isolated. Again, you can ask the person running your group for suggestions.

Read a Gospel

If you've enjoyed reading and thinking about the Bible as part of *Wonderfully Made*, you don't need to stop now! There's lots more to discover. A good place to start is with one of the biographies of Jesus (known as the four Gospels): Matthew, Mark, Luke or John. If you don't have a Bible, your group leader will be happy to lend you one or give you a Gospel to read.

Take another short course

Lots of churches run courses for people who want to find out more about what Christianity really is, like *Christianity Explored* or *Alpha*. Your group leader will be able to tell you if your local church is running one soon. You could even get together with others from your toddler group and do the course at a time which suits you.

You might appreciate the opportunity to take another, more substantial parenting course—especially if you have older children too. Your local church might be able to run a community parenting course, such as *Putting parenting to bed*.

One life.
What's it all about?

Christianity
E✝PLORED

Christianity Explored is a course run by many churches which gives you time and space to think about the big questions of life and to consider the life of the person at the heart of the Christian faith - Jesus Christ. Over seven weeks you'll discover who Jesus is, why he came and what it means to follow him as you journey through Mark's Gospel. Sessions usually last a couple of hours and often include food, drink and a time to chat and relax. A short DVD or talk and a discussion time where you can ask questions, or simply sit and listen to others. You can say as much or as little as you like. And don't worry—you'll never be asked to sing, pray or read aloud. You don't need to know anything about the Bible either.

To find out if there is a course near you, go to www.christianityexplored.org

www.christianityexplored.org

CHRISTIANITY
E✝PLORED
MINISTRIES

Children's Bibles

The Beginner's Bible

Containing, a good mixture of stories and accurate illustrations with key Bible themes linking them together, this is our top recommendation for a story Bible for children under six.

The Jesus Storybook Bible

SALLY LLOYD-JONES & JAGO

The Jesus Storybook Bible shows how everything in the Bible, from the stories of Noah to Moses to the great King David, is about Jesus Christ. Every story whispers his name.

The Big Picture Story Bible

DAVID HELM

The Big Picture Story Bible presents the remarkable true story of God's love for the world. Simple words and striking illustrations unfold the storyline of God's word from Genesis to Revelation.

International Children's Bible
(New Century Version)

Our pick as the best available junior Bible. Translated directly from the original texts into English that can be read and understood by children aged between 6 and 12. It has large, easy-to-read type in two columns, over 40 pages of maps and illustrations, and a dictionary.

www.thegoodbook.co.uk/bibles/childrens

putting parenting to bed

Being a parent to small children can be frustrating and exhausting. There are so many questions that need answering: what's the best way to encourage and to discipline children? How do I know if I'm doing well as a parent? How do you raise a child? These are some of the many questions looked at in *Putting Parenting to Bed*, a short course that's packed with common-sense parenting advice that's based on biblical principles.
As well as liberating confused parents to enjoy their children and the adventure of raising them, this course aims to make people think about the bigger questions of life.

www.thegoodbook.co.uk/pptbs

The ONE O'CLOCK MIRACLE

This stunning hardback storybook for children aged 3-6 has been illustrated by Catalina Echeverri (illustrator of *Monty's Christmas* for John Lewis). It brings to life the healing of the official's son in John chapter 4 and teaches children to trust the words of Jesus because he is God's Son.

www.thegoodbook.co.uk/toom

thegoodbook
COMPANY
Opening up the Bible

At The Good Book Company, we are dedicated to helping people understand what Christianity is, and to helping Christians and local churches grow. We believe that God's growth process always starts with hearing clearly what he has said to us through his timeless word—the Bible.

Ever since we opened our doors in 1991, we have been striving to produce resources that honour God in the way the Bible is used. We have grown to become an international provider of user-friendly resources, with people of all backgrounds and denominations using our books, courses and DVDs.

We want to enable people to understand who Jesus is; and to equip ordinary Christians to live for him day by day, and churches to grow in their knowledge of God and in their love for one another and their neighbours.

Call us for a discussion of your needs or visit one of our local websites for more information on the resources and services we provide.

UK & Europe: www.thegoodbook.co.uk
North America: www.thegoodbook.com
Australia: www.thegoodbook.com.au
New Zealand: www.thegoodbook.co.nz

UK & Europe: 0333 123 0880
North America: 866 244 2165
Australia: (02) 6100 4211
New Zealand (+64) 3 343 1990